MAXIMUM
RIDE

MAXIMUM RIDE

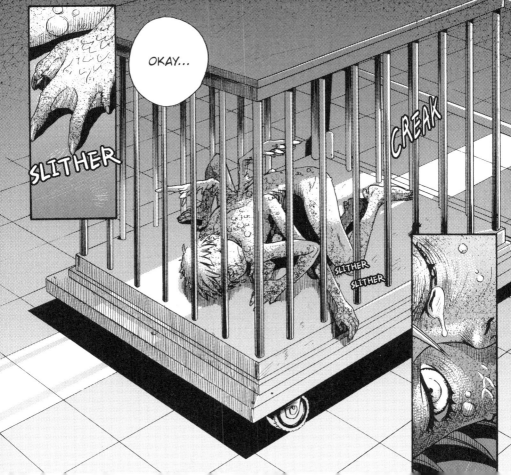

YOU'RE THE ONE WHO'S THEIR DOG!

HMPH

WHY DON'T YOU GET YOUR LEASH AND BEG FOR A WALK YOURSELF?

SPIN

?!

SHUT UP!

WHAM

WHAM

ARI!!

ACK!

WHAM

WATCH IT.

TSK!

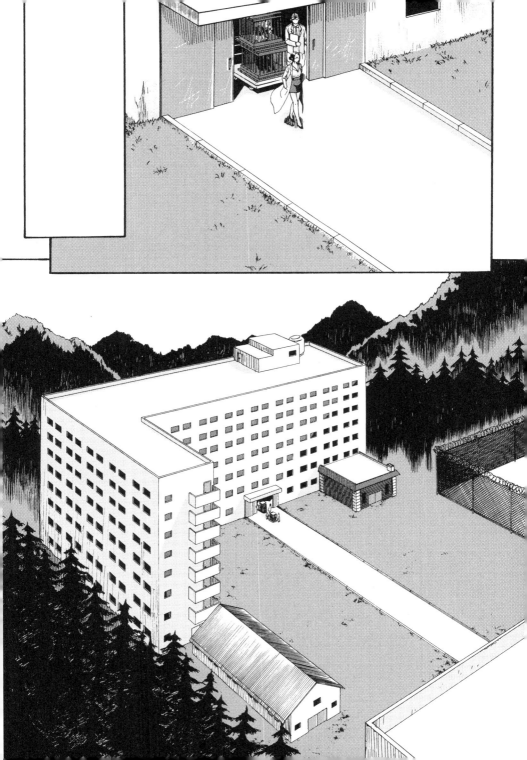

19

GRRR

ROAR!

?!

AIEEE!!

WHAT A SHOW.

MAXIMUM!

MAX! PLEASE!

YOU WERE SAFE HERE! THIS WAS ONLY A TEST!

YOU HAVE TO TRUST ME— I'M THE ONLY ONE YOU CAN TRUST!

PLEASE! COME BACK! MAX!!

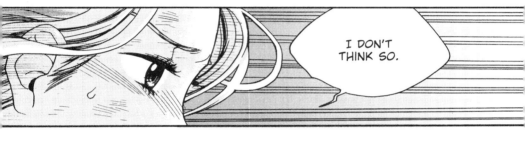

I DON'T
THINK SO.

JEB...

...KNOWS WHERE OUR HOUSE IS.

WE CAN'T EVER GO BACK. WE NEED A NEW HOME.

NOD

YES...

MAXIMUM
RIDE
CHAPTER 9

YOU'RE SO
SLOW.

TSK.

NO,
JUST AT
EASE.

IGGY!
GAZZY!

GAZZY!

FINALLY, WE
ESCAPED THE
HOUNDS OF HELL
AT THE SCHOOL,
AND WE HAD
ANGEL BACK.

WE WERE
HOMELESS,
AIMLESS, ON
THE RUN...

...BUT
I FELT
HAPPY.

THE SIX
OF US WERE
TOGETHER,
AND WE WERE
FLYING ABOVE
THE CLOUDS
IN THE BLUE,
BLUE SKY.

WHAT? LIKE, WHERE THEY GOT THE DNA?

...YEAH...

WELL, SPILL IT!

RUSTLE

IGGY...

THEY HAVE FILES ON US. LIKE, THE MAIN FILES.

THEY'RE IN NEW YORK. AT A PLACE CALLED "THE INSTITUTE."

THE INSTITUTE? IN NEW YORK CITY OR UPSTATE NEW YORK?

I DON'T KNOW. I *THINK* IT WAS CALLED THE INSTITUTE. THE LIVING INSTITUTE OR SOMETHING.

I HEARD— I HEARD THAT THEY TOLD NUDGE'S MOM AND DAD THAT SHE HAD DIED.

I *DID* HAVE A MOM AND DAD.

BUT SHE HADN'T.

I DID!

...DIED.

AND... IGGY'S MOM...

SHE DIED WHEN HE WAS BORN.

53

MAX, I'VE BEEN THINKING ABOUT MY MOM AND DAD.

HMM?

I BET—IF THEY'VE BEEN THINKING I DIED ELEVEN YEARS AGO, THEN I BET THEY WOULD BE PRETTY HAPPY TO SEE ME, WOULDN'T THEY?

UNLESS...I MEAN—I GUESS I'M NOT WHAT THEY WOULD BE EXPECTING, HUH? IT'S NOT MY FAULT OR ANYTHING, BUT, I MEAN, I'VE GOT *WINGS*.

THEY MIGHT NOT WANT ME IF I HAVE WINGS AND AM SO WEIRD AND ALL.

I DON'T KNOW, NUDGE.

MAX, WAKE UP.

HMM...?

...YOU'RE RIGHT...

DAMN...THEY REALLY DON'T LET US REST, DO THEY...?

THREE... ...NO, FOUR OF THEM...

...TWO MORE...

MAXIMUM
RIDE
CHAPTER 10

THIS WAY!

STUDENTS' DAY AT THE CENTRAL PARK ZOO

LET'S MERGE IN.

SORRY.

WATCH IT.

SHUP!

STUDENTS' DAY ONLY. NO UNAUTHORIZED ADULTS. SHOW ME YOUR PASS IF YOU'RE A CHAPERONE.

→HUFF←

→HUFF←

GRRR

TCH!

IT LOOKS LIKE THEY CAN'T GET IN.

LET'S TAKE A BREATHER.

WOW— LOOK!

SLURP

YOU KNOW WHAT I LIKE ABOUT NEW YORK?

IT'S FULL OF NEW YORKERS WHO ARE FREAKIER THAN WE ARE.

IT'S ALREADY THREE...

WE CAN'T JUST KEEP WALKING FOREVER...

DO YOU HAVE A PLAN?

SO WE BLEND?

CAN WE TAKE THE SUBWAY TO THE PARK? I'M SO TIRED.

ME TOO—

MAX... I'M TIRED TOO.

IT'S ONLY EIGHTEEN BLOCKS.

UGH

......

...OKAY...

YAY~

WHAT IS THIS? WHY ISN'T IT COMING?

IT'S ONLY BEEN TEN MINUTES.

HMM? DO YOU HEAR THAT? IT SOUNDS LIKE VOICES.

DON'T SAY THAT!! WE'RE THE ONLY ONES HERE!! SCARY—!!

!

NO...

I THINK IGGY'S RIGHT. I HEAR IT TOO.

NOOO~ NOT YOU TOO, MAX~!

WHERE ARE YOU GOING?

JUST FOLLOW ME!

TA
TA
TA

ISN'T IT THE WORKERS?

DON'T BE STUPID.

ARE WE GONNA MEET THE RAT MASTER AND BECOME NINJA-EAGLES OR SOMETHING?

SSK

WHAT'S THIS...?

I'M A LITTLE SCARED...

WHISPER WHISPER

WHOA, IT'S LIKE AN UNDER- GROUND CITY!

I THINK IT MIGHT BE NICE TO STAY HERE TONIGHT.

SWISH

WHAT DO YOU THINK?

UGH...

THROB
THROB

MAX? YOU
OKAY?

YEAH, I'LL
BE BETTER
TOMORROW.

FEELS
LIKE MY
HEAD'S
GONNA
EXPLODE!

WHO'S
SCREWING
WITH MY
MAC?

WHAT MAKES YOU THINK THAT?

You think I'm stupid?

LET ME SEE. MAYBE BECAUSE YOU'RE A BUNCH OF *KIDS* SLEEPIN' IN A *SUBWAY TUNNEL*. KIND OF CLUES ME IN, YOU KNOW?

......

What's going on?

WHAT ABOUT YOU? YOU'RE A KID SLEEPING IN A SUBWAY TUNNEL. DON'T YOU HAVE SCHOOL?

M.I.T. KICKED ME OUT. I GOT EARLY ADMISSION. WAS GONNA MAJOR IN COMPUTER TECHNOLOGY.

PAT PAT

BUT I WOULDN'T TAKE MY THORAZINE.

THEY SAID, NO THORAZINE, NO SCHOOL.

WHAT'S THORAZINE?

I SAW IT AT THE SCHOOL. IT'S WHAT THEY GIVE SCHIZO-PHRENICS.

NO HALDOL, NO MELLERIL, NO ZYPREXA. THEY ALL SUCK.

PEOPLE JUST WANT ME TO BE QUIET, DO WHAT I'M TOLD, DON'T MAKE TROUBLE.

......

IT'S MY BREAD AND BUTTER.

I CAN HACK INTO ANYTHING. SOMETIMES PEOPLE PAY ME.

SO WHAT'S UP WITH YOUR COMPUTER?

I DO JOBS WHEN I NEED MON—

WHY? WHO WANTS TO KNOW?

?

93

GET ON THE MADISON AVENUE BUS.

THROB THROB

URG...

GET OFF WHEN IT LOOKS LIKE FUN.

M1
M2
M3

MAX...?

WOW, LOOK AT THAT!

SO THIS IS A BUS! IT'S SO BIG!

DON'T BE SUCH A BUMPKIN!

...so embarrassing...

Ssk

OH MAN... WE'RE DANGEROUSLY LOW ON CASH NOW...

SO...WHERE ARE WE GOING, MAX?

SHUDDER

HUH?!

IT'S JUST...THE VOICE TOLD ME TO TAKE THIS BUS...I DIDN'T HAVE ANY OTHER PLAN.

VOICE?
LIKE YOUR
CONSCIENCE?

...DUNNO.

MAX HAS NO
CONSCIENCE!
SHE ONCE ATE
MY CAKE WHILE
I WAS GONE!

HA-HA...
YEAH, YOUR
FACE WAS
HILARIOUS
WHEN YOU
FOUND OUT.

I remember!

...HE'S SO
STINGY.

WELL,
VOICE?
WHAT NOW?

DO YOU
HEAR THAT,
VOICE? IF YOU'RE
GOING TO MAKE
ME LET EVERY-
ONE DOWN...

...YOU'RE GOING
TO BE SORRY YOU
EVER...ENTERED
MY BRAIN.

SMILE

I'LL BUY IT FOR YOU.

......

YAY! ♡ THANK YOU, THANK YOU SO MUCH!

HERE'S YOUR RECEIPT.

MAX, LOOK...

WHAT WAS THAT ABOUT? HOW DID YOU...?

WHAT DID YOU SAY TO HER?

SO YOU JUST ASKED A STRANGER TO BUY YOU AN EXPENSIVE TOY, AND SHE DID?

NOTHING. I JUST ASKED HER IF SHE WOULD BUY ME THIS BEAR, 'COS I REALLY WANTED IT AND I DIDN'T HAVE ENOUGH MONEY.

YEAH, I JUST ASKED HER TO BUY IT FOR ME.

YOU KNOW...

104

...WITH MY MIND.

AND SHE SAID OKAY.

I'M GOING TO CALL IT CELESTE.

ANGEL, ARE YOU SAYING YOU INFLUENCED THAT WOMAN SO SHE WOULD BUY YOU THE BEAR?

CELESTE. WHAT'S "INFLU-ENCED"?

LET'S GET OUT OF HERE FIRST.

......

OKAY.

SHE'S BEEN ACTING OUT OF CHARAC-TER TODAY.

AND SHE SHOULD KNOW INFLUENCING SOMEONE IS WRONG...THIS IS DISTURBING.

ARE YOU HEARING...

WE NEED TO FIND THE INSTITUTE! WE'RE RUNNING OUT OF MONEY!

OF COURSE I'M NOT RELAXING!

AND WE'RE CONSTANTLY IN DANGER!

SILENCE...

TAP

WHAT'S WRONG, MAX?

CAL—

CALM DOWN.

111

PHEW... WHAT A DAY.

MAYBE THE INSTITUTE IS IN ANOTHER DIMENSION OR SOMETHING...

Tip!

Ssk

MAYBE... SIGH.

WHAT'S THIS?

It is unlawful to climb trees in Central Park.

Please come down at once.

HOW DID THEY KNOW WE WERE UP HERE?

WHO LOOKS UP INTO A TREE?

OKAY, GUYS. GET DOWN; TRY TO LOOK *NORMAL*. WHEN WE'RE ON THE GROUND, WE'LL MAKE A RUN FOR IT.

IF WE GET SEPARATED, CONNECT UP AT, LIKE, FIFTY-FOURTH STREET AND FIFTH AVENUE.

Again, please come down at once.

OKAY, OKAY...

SORRY—

THERE ARE SIGNS POSTED EVERYWHERE CLEARLY STATING THAT CLIMBING TREES IS FORBIDDEN.

AH!

NOW!

SSK

CELESTE!

......

CELESTE!

BRING CELESTE BACK!

I'LL GET YOU ANOTHER ONE.

I DON'T WANT ANOTHER ONE!

I'M SORRY, BUT WE NEED TO HIDE, SO WE CAN'T GO BACK.

MAX, WHAT'S THAT?

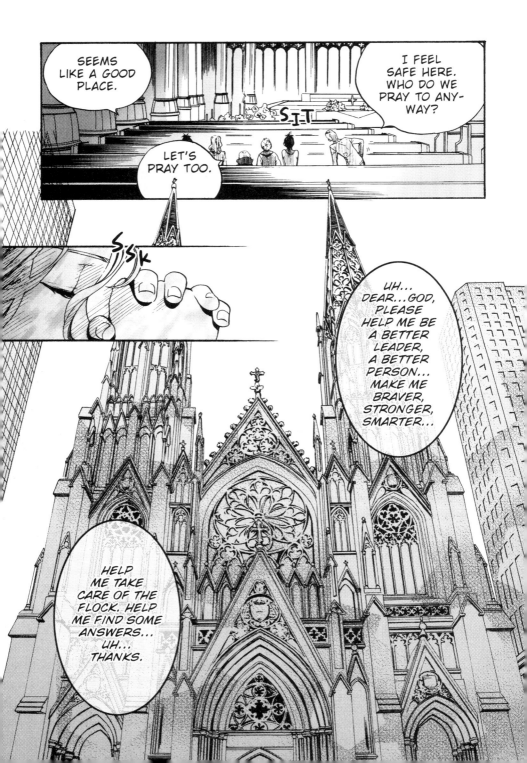

MAXIMUM
RIDE

NO.

JUST THAT
BUILDING.

THEN...

...THAT
MEANS...

LET'S TRY
LOOKING FOR
IT FIRST.

RUB
RUB

TAP

HERE.

2901
2902
2903
2904

1004 P
1005 C.C.C
1006 YEN PRESS
1007 HAKUSAN

INSTITUTE
...FOR...
HIGHER...
LIVING...

CNT insurance   2902
FILL SYSTEM   2904

1003 NFN
1004 panasonic
1005 C.C.C

IT'S NOT ON THE DIRECTORY.

EXCUSE ME, ARE THERE ANY OTHER COMPANIES IN THIS BUILDING THAT AREN'T LISTED?

NO.

......

TAPPA

TAPPA TAPPA

NOW WHAT—

EEK!

WHAT IS THIS?!

WHAT'S WRONG?

I'VE BEEN WORKING ON THAT FILE ALL DAY...

There's a pot of gold beneath every rainbow

GASP!

DOES THIS BUILDING HAVE A BASEMENT?

TSK.

WHO ARE YOU? WHAT DO YOU WANT?

......

NEVER MIND.

I THINK THAT CAN BE ARRANGED.

WHOA!

MAY I HELP YOU? ARE YOU WAITING FOR YOUR PARENTS?

NO, IT'S JUST US.

UM, OKAY...

GLANCE

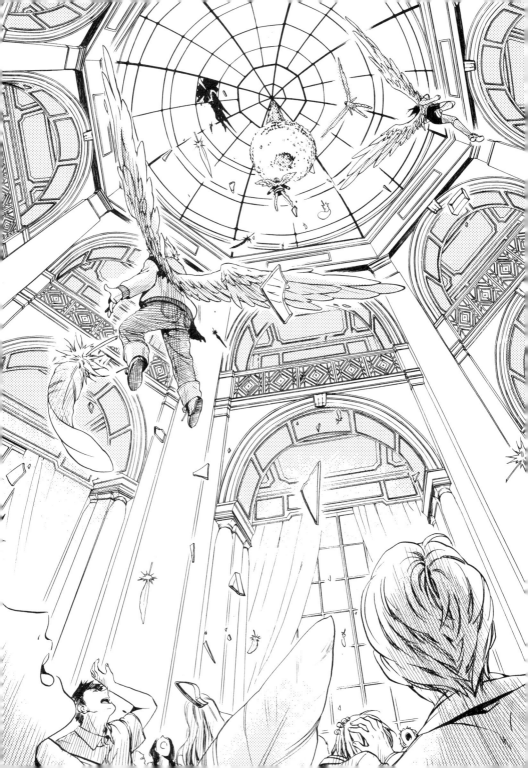

AH, THAT
FELT GOOD,
TO FLY OUT
LIKE THAT!!

...I'M SORRY, IT WAS MY FAULT.

I'M THE ONE WHO WANTED TO GO THERE.

IT WAS THEIR FAULT, GAZZY. NO NEED TO APOLOGIZE.

IT'S FOR THE BEST.

I BET THOSE WEREN'T EVEN REAL COPS. THEY HAD AN "EAU DE SCHOOL" AIR ABOUT THEM.

MAXIMUM RIDE

CHAPTER 13

C—

ANGEL, NO!

CELESTE! DASH!

TAP

FWOOSH!

ANGEL!!

TAP

COME BACK HERE, ANGEL...

SSK

AND ANGEL...HER TELEPATHIC POWERS SEEM TO BE GROWING...

WHAT IN THE WORLD IS HAPPENING WITH HER?

DON'T BORROW TROUBLE, MAX.

H'MPH

YOU AGAIN...

WORRY IS UNPRODUCTIVE. YOU CAN'T CONTROL WHAT HAPPENS TO ANGEL.

YOU CAN SAVE THE WORLD, BUT THE ONLY THING YOU CAN CONTROL IS YOU.

GO TO SLEEP, MAX. IT'S TIME TO LEARN.

AH...

NEW YORK POST

MIRACLE OR ILLUSION? SUPERHUMANS OR GENETIC FREAKS?

No one has taken credit for what may be this year's most incredible stunt...

TH-THIS IS...

SAW THEM WHEN WE WERE OUT. GUESS WE BETTER LIE LOW FOR A WHILE.

WELL, SO I WAS THINKING—

WHAT'S THIS?

WE'RE HAVING A MAKEOVER FEST!

YOU GUYS CAN HAVE TOTAL MAKEOVERS FOR FREE—AS LONG AS YOUR STYLIST GETS TO DO WHATEVER HE OR SHE WANTS.

ISN'T THIS COOL, MAX?! AND IT'S FREE!

I FOUND IT ON OUR WAY BACK FROM GETTING BREAKFAST!

GOOD JOB, NUDGE!!

PAT PAT

HEH HEH.

LET'S DO THIS!

TAP

YAY

AH...

HMM...

SHUDDER!!

THEY LOOK THE SAME. IS THAT YOUR UNIFORM?

WHAT ABOUT YOU? ALL BLACK AGAIN?

...THE DESIGN'S DIFFERENT.

MAX, FANG, LOOK!

175

NO ONE WILL RECOGNIZE US, RIGHT?

WE LOOK SO BAD IN THE PHOTO HERE.

MAX IS TAKING A LONG TIME.

MAX! THERE YOU ARE.

SSK

SORRY TO KEEP YOU WAITING.

HA-HA...

WOW— LOOK AT YOUR HAIR! IT'S COOL!

YOU LOOK LIKE AN ADULT... LIKE TWENTY-THREE?

TH-THANKS, NUDGE.

SEEMS A BIT LATE TO SEARCH FOR THE INSTITUTE.

IT'S ALREADY GETTING DARK.

HMM...

MAX, GUESS WHAT!

ANGEL!!

I CAN BREATHE UNDER-WATER!!

WHAT?!

......?!

TH-THEN I BET I CAN DO IT TOO! 'COS WE'RE SIBLINGS!!

CUT IT OUT, GAZZY!

PWAH!!

TOLD YOU SO...

......

SHE CAN BREATHE UNDERWATER... OUR ABILITIES KEEP UNFOLDING...

JUST SWALLOW THE WATER AND BLOW THE AIR OUT.

...AS IF THEY'D BEEN PROGRAMMED TO COME OUT AT DIFFERENT TIMES...HOW WEIRD...

REALLY?

NOT WEIRD, MAX. DIVINE. AND BRILLIANT.

YOU SIX ARE WORKS OF ART. ENJOY IT.

WORKS OF ART? OR FREAKS?

WHAT DO YOU WISH YOU COULD DO, MAX? IF YOU COULD DO ANYTHING?

MAXIMUM
RIDE

A MUTANT FREAK AND A HERO...

'KAY...

FANG.

?

...ACTUALLY MIGHT NOT BE THAT DIFFERENT...

......

SAVE THE WORLD, MAX.

WHAT'S WRONG? THE VOICE IN YOUR HEAD?

NOT NOW.

SMUSH!

THEN GET SOME SLEEP.

Don't waste your energy overthinking things.

MAXIMUM RIDE
CHAPTER 14

......

GUESS THAT'S A GOOD IDEA.

GOOD MORNING.

OR MAYBE, GOOD NIGHT?

ARI!

DAMMIT...

WHERE'RE THE REST? YOU ON A DATE OR SOMETHING?

THERE'RE MORE THAN I'VE EVER SEEN BEFORE!

I CAN STILL SMELL CHICKEN OVER THERE, SO THERE'S NO USE HIDING!

!!

HMPH... ALL A DOG CAN DO IS SNIFF AROUND, RIGHT?!

SHUT UP!

U AND A, NOW!!

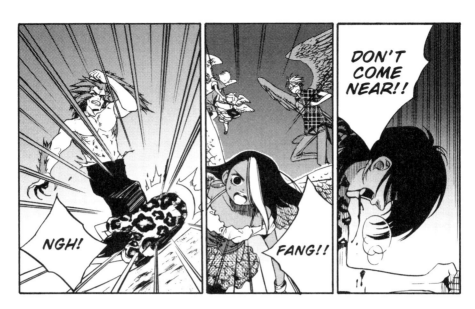

NGH!

FANG!!

DON'T COME NEAR!!

FANG...

HA... HOW VERY...

SSK

CRASH!!

...TOUCH-ING!!

THUD

FANG—!!

FANG, WAKE UP!!

TAP
TAP
TAP

HAD ENOUGH OF LIFE? HEH-HEH.

LEAVE HIM ALONE!

ARI.

SSk

SHFF

STOP.

!

YOU HAVE YOUR ORDERS.

TCH!

......

JEB.

DO YOU GET IT NOW...

...MAX?

NO ONE HAS EVER EXPERIENCED ANYTHING LIKE WHAT YOU'RE FEELING.

DO YOU SEE WHY ALL THIS IS NECESSARY?

204

? ?

UH-UH-UH...

!!

BLUSH!

HUH?

HA...

HA HA...

→COUGH←

COUGH...

...THIS FEELS PRETTY BAD.

LET'S FIND A PLACE TO HUNKER DOWN.

Y-YEAH.

LET ME HEL—

FANG, HOW'RE YOU FEELING?

AH... I'M COOL...

AHEM.

......

If only I could erase memories...

UM...

F-FANG...

...ABOUT WHAT HAPPENED BEFORE—

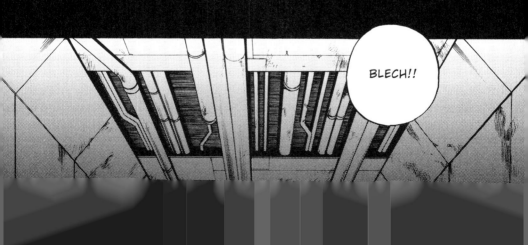

KWAM

HOW DO WE...

...OPE—

SPLOOSH

WOW, A DOOR IN THE SEWER WALL...

BUT OF COURSE, IT'S LOCKED.

KA-CHAK

KICK THIS OPEN TOO, MAX.

TAP TAP

THIS WILL BE A PIECE OF CAKE.

ANGEL!

HUH?

SSK

LET ME
BORROW
THIS.

CLATTER
CLATTER

CREAK

DONE!

CREAK

GULP

YOU'RE ON YOUR OWN NOW, MAX.

WHAT'S THAT SUPPOSED TO MEAN?

 CLICK

SEE YOU LATER.

CREAK

ANOTHER HURDLE.

password

OKAY, GUYS. LET'S FIND A WAY TO CRACK...

BA-DUMP

SHUDDER!

BA-DUMP

...THE PASS-WORD...

UM, TRY BIG "X," LITTLE "J"...

...BIG "H," LITTLE "J," AND THE NUMBER FOUR?

...LITTLE "N," BIG "P"...

...NUMBER SEVEN, BIG "O"...

WELCOM!

!!

IT WORKED! WHERE'D YOU GET IT?

UM? THE COM- PUT- ER.

SSK

IT'S A WOMAN, WITH FRIZZY RED HAIR. SHE TYPED IN THE PASS- WORD, AND I CAN FEEL IT.

SHAAA...

LIKE, WHEN I TOUCH IT, I CAN SEE THE PERSON WHO WORKS HERE.

WOW. TOUCH SOMETHING ELSE!

SORRY TO INTERRUPT, BUT LOOK AT THIS FOLDER.

AH, RIGHT. THIS ONE...?

OH GOD, OH GOD. THIS IS IT!

YOU THINK WE CAN PRINT IT?

THESE CURTAINS ARE HUGE. WHAT'S BEHIND THEM?

HMM... MAYBE THE REAL PASSAGE?

AH...

MAXIMUM
RIDE

UH, JUST A SECOND, MAX.

LOOK!

SLIDE!

WHAT THE...?

WHAT IS THIS...?

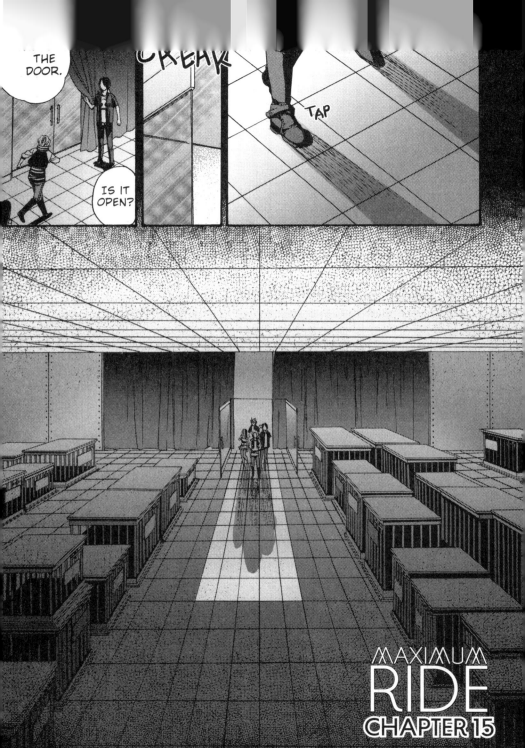

SWISH

......

HOW COULD THERE BE SO MANY—

?

THIS IS...PA-THETIC.

SSK

HI, DOGGIE.

YOU LOOK LIKE TOTO FROM *THE WIZARD OF OZ.*

PANT
PANT

SHIVER SHIVER...

DOES SHE KNOW ARI?

LEAD THEM OUT, FANG. I'LL BUY US SOME TIME.

'KAY.

BACK AGAIN, ARI?

DIDN'T EXPECT TO SEE YOU SO SOON.

WHAT ARE YOU DOING HERE?

I THOUGHT DAD WAS KEEPING YOU ON A SHORT LEASH.

GRR...

SO WHAT HAPPENED, ARI,

WHO TOOK CARE OF YOU WHEN JEB LEFT WITH US?

THE WHITE COATS.

I NEED TO KEEP HIS ATTENTION ON ME.

DON'T WORRY ABOUT IT; I WAS IN GOOD HANDS. THE BEST. SOMEBODY WAS LOOKING AFTER ME.

ARI.

DID JEB GIVE THEM PERMISSION TO ERASERFY YOU, OR DID SOMEONE JUST DO IT...

...WHILE HE WAS GONE?

WHAT DO YOU CARE?

YOU'RE SO PERFECT, THE ONE SUCCESSFUL RECOMBINANT. AND I'M NOBODY, THE BOY WHO WAS LEFT BEHIND.

...SOMEONE DID TERRIBLE THINGS TO YOU BECAUSE JEB WASN'T THERE TO PROTECT YOU.

MAYBE SOMEONE WANTED TO SEE IF ERASERS WOULD LAST LONGER IF THEY DIDN'T START FROM INFANCY.

SHUT UP!

SPLASH!

PHEW...

FACE IT, ARI. YOU'RE NOT JUST A BIG, HAIRY SEVEN-YEAR-OLD.

YOU...!

GRRR...

YOU'RE MUCH MORE OF AN OBVIOUS MUTANT FREAK THAN I AM. AND YOUR OWN FATHER LET IT HAPPEN.

SPLOOSH!

I SAID, SHUT UP!

!!

SLIIIDE

THUD!

CRACK

DAMN, THE FLOOR IS AS SLIPPERY AS YOU!!

SPLASH!

SPLASH!

TCH!

SWISH!

WHAM!!

KOFF!

GRAB

YOU MIGHT BE FASTER IN THE SKY...

...BUT I'M FASTER ON THE GROUND, YOU KNOW?

THUD!!

AH...

...NGH.

YOU REALLY HURT ME...

SSK

SPLASH!

SEEP

CLENCH

I WOULDN'T HURT YOU, NOT LIKE THIS.

MAX? WHAT WAS THAT?

ARE YOU OKAY?

I-I... I THINK I BROKE HIS NECK.

BA-DUMP!

I-IS HE DEAD?

EVERY-ONE'S OUT, AND IT'S ONLY US LEFT. LET'S GET OUT OF HERE!

AH... YEAH...

SPLASH!

SPLASH!

SPLASH!

CAN HE... REALLY BE DEAD?!

BA-DUMP

BA-DUMP BA-DUMP

FLINCH!

THERE!!

FANG!!

THIS
WAY!

SHUDDER!

HE WAS
MY SON!!

≻PANT≺

≻PANT≺

......

JEB!!!

WHY ARE YOU DOING THIS?

TREMBLE TREMBLE

WHY THIS GAME? THIS TEST? LOOK AT WHAT YOU'VE DONE!!

PANT

PANT

MAX, YOU WANT ANSWERS TO THE SECRETS OF LIFE, AND THAT'S NOT HOW IT WORKS.

NOT FOR ANYBODY, NOT EVEN YOU.

......

YOU KILLED YOUR OWN BROTHER!

IS SOMETHING BOTHERING YOU?

AH... NO.

WHERE ARE THE OTHER KIDS?

THE GIRL WITH WINGS TOOK THEM.

SHE DIDN'T WANT TO STAY WITH US.

HRM. SAY, CELESTE LOOKS BLACK...MAYBE YOU SHOULD GIVE HER A SHOW—

WAIT, WHAT IS THAT?!

IT'S MY DOG.

YOUR WHAT?

HE'S MY DOG, TOTAL.

TOTAL?!

THAT'S WHAT HIS CARD SAID.

ANGEL—

NO! HE'S STAYING!

I DIDN'T EVEN SAY ANYTHING...

YOU TRY.

......

ANGEL...

TWINKLE

TWINKLE

SO...

FANG...

BUT...

......

THE FIRST TIME YOU DON'T TAKE CARE OF HIM, HE'S OUT.

WHAT?!

SHE MADE BAMBI EYES AT ME...

TOTAL! YOU CAN STAY!

...I KNOW WHAT YOU MEAN.

SPIN

SPIN

LEAP!!

WOOF!!

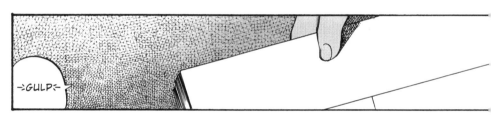

AH!!

HERE I AM! MY NAME! AN ADDRESS!

VIRGINIA! IT'S IN VIRGINIA!

I'VE GOT AN ADDRESS TOO, AND SOME NAMES. AND, OH MAN, THERE ARE PICTURES.

LET US SEE, LET US SEE!

HE LOOKS JUST LIKE YOU, FANG. AND SO DOES SHE.

THEY'VE GOT TO BE YOUR MOM AND DAD!

...MAYBE, MAYBE NOT.

ANGEL! LOOK! IT'S A PICTURE OF OUR PARENTS!

REALLY?!

THIS IS ME...

YOU KNOW WHAT? ALL THE ADDRESSES ARE IN VIRGINIA AND MARYLAND AND WASHINGTON, D.C. THEY'RE ALL KINDA CLOSE, RIGHT?

ARE THEY FAR FROM HERE?

SO WHAT ARE WE GOING TO DO?

......

HMM...

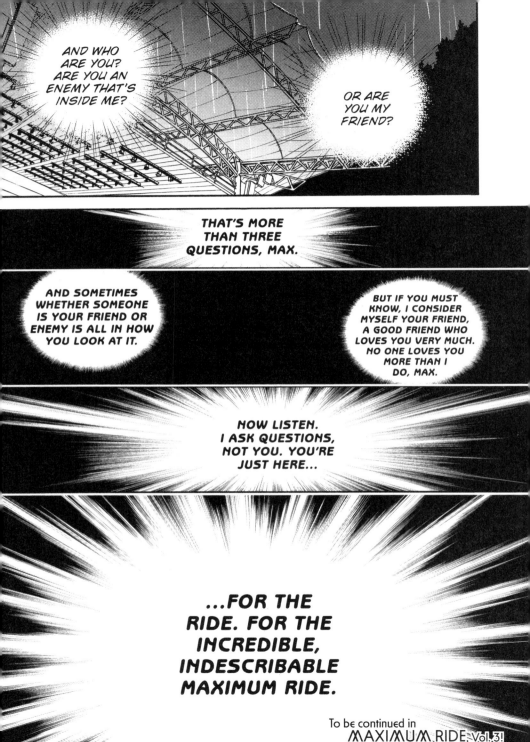